WONDERMOUSE
AND OTHER STORIES

Wondermouse

The Great Lying Contest

The Nightmare   10

The Great Jumping Contest   21

The Filthy Stranger   30

One Good Turn Deserves Another   34

The Giant in the Bottle   49

CHRISTOPHER WALKER

Nelson

Wondermouse

Max Mouse was often bored. He looked at the other mice. They all did the same things. All they did was steal cheese, eat it, sleep and hide from cats.

"If only one mouse would do something different," he thought.

As he said this, he saw that all the mice were doing the same thing. They were chewing bits off a great piece of cheese that they had stolen the night before.

2

"Surely you can do other things with cheese as well as eat it," thought Max.

And do you know what he did? He hung upside down by his tail from the branch of a tree. Then he stuffed cheese down his ears till they were both full.

The younger mice saw this. "Great!" they said. And they hung by their tails and stuffed cheese down their ears.

Next day the younger mice said to Max, "You are different. You must be our leader."

Max had to scrape the cheese out of one ear so that he could hear what they said.

They went on. "Do something else for us that is different," they said.

"Follow me," said Max. He didn't know what he was going to do, so he led them into town.

Mrs Jones was just getting into her car.

Now Max knew that many ladies are scared by mice. So he jumped into Mrs Jones' car. Mrs Jones screamed and jumped out of the car just as it started off. Max jumped onto the steering wheel. He was scared out of his wits. The car went off down the road, but soon came to a halt because it had run out of petrol.

That night the younger mice said, "What a leader! He can drive a car. No mouse has ever done such a thing before."

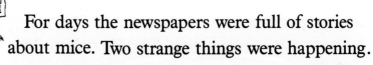

For days the newspapers were full of stories about mice. Two strange things were happening.

Cats were killing young mice all over town. The cats had never had it so good. The mice had their ears stuffed with cheese. They didn't hear the cats coming until it was too late.

The other strange news was that mice kept jumping into people's cars. All over town ladies were leaping from their cars. The town was full of dead mice and wrecked cars.

Soon there were not many young mice left. Those who survived said to Max, "Oh leader. Do something else that is different."

"Follow me," said Max.

Again he did not know what he was going to do so he led them into town. The first shop they came to was a music shop. It was full of pianos and organs. The man had just switched on a self-playing piano. Max climbed on just as it started playing. He was so frightened that he raced up and down along the keys until the music stopped.

"What a leader!" the astonished mice said.

For days the newspapers had more odd stories about mice. Mice were flinging themselves on pianos all over town.

Max was starting to lose his nerve. He was
sorry he had started to do things that were
different. He put on dark glasses so that the
other mice would not recognise him. He still
had one ear full of cheese, which is why,
that night,
the cat killed him so easily.

Max never saw him and only heard him when
it was too late.

The mice erected a statue to him. It read:

WONDERMOUSE
He could play the piano
He could drive a car
There never was a mouse like Wondermouse

But the cat found that he tasted just like any other young mouse. (Except that he had cheese down only one ear.)

The Great Lying Contest

In a land far away, the winters were very long.
The snow lay on the ground for months. The
King, who loved hunting, was trapped in his
palace. No one could hunt in such weather.

The King grew extremely bored. He had
heard all the jokes of his jesters. They no
longer made him laugh.

The King sent for his wise men. They told him tales of long ago. Soon the King was bored with these tales too.

"Are these tales true?" asked the King.

"They are, sir," the wise men said.

The King said, "If the truth is so dull, I would rather listen to lies."

As he said this, a great idea came into his mind. "This should be fun," he chuckled.

The King sent for his heralds.

"Go to every house in the land. This is what you must say to all the people. The King wants to find the best liar in the kingdom. The prize for the biggest lie will be the King's own crown. It is of solid gold and is studded with jewels."

There were many liars in that country. From every town and village they came to the palace. The snow did not stop them. Each one told lies to the King.

Now kings are used to flattery. This is a kind
of lying. He listened to every lie, but he was sure
he had heard bigger lies before. He now began
to be bored with such poor lies. He decided
to stop the contest because no winner could
be found.

Just then, a poor man dressed in rags came up
to him. He carried a large, empty sack.

"What do you want?" asked the King.

The man looked puzzled. "You haven't forgotten, sir?" he asked. "You owe me a sackful of gold. Remember? I have come to pick it up."

"That's the biggest lie I ever heard," said the King. "I don't owe you any gold."

"If mine is the biggest lie," said the man, "then I have won the contest. Give me your golden crown."

The King changed his mind. "No! You are not a liar," he said.

"In that case, it must be true that you owe me a sackful of gold," said the man. "May I have it now, please?" And he held out the empty sack.

The King saw that either way he could not win. When the man left the palace his sack was no longer empty. It contained the crown which the King was forced to give him.

The great lying contest was over.

The Nightmare

Mr Brown ate a big lunch every day. Except on Sundays. Then the lunch wasn't just big.
It was **ENORMOUS**.

One Sunday, Mr Brown had a huge plate of roast beef.
And Yorkshire pudding.
And boiled potatoes.
And roast potatoes.
And peas.
And carrots.
And gravy.

After that he had apple pie and cream.

Then Mrs Brown said to him, "I'll make some coffee. You have a little nap. I'll wake you when the coffee is ready."

But Mr Brown did not hear her. He was already fast asleep. He lay with his head back on the settee. His mouth was wide open.

Soon he was snoring loudly.

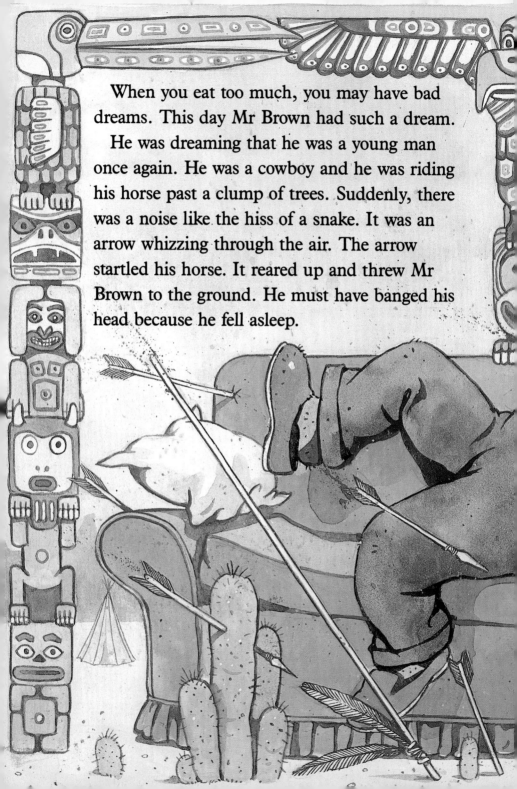

When you eat too much, you may have bad dreams. This day Mr Brown had such a dream.

He was dreaming that he was a young man once again. He was a cowboy and he was riding his horse past a clump of trees. Suddenly, there was a noise like the hiss of a snake. It was an arrow whizzing through the air. The arrow startled his horse. It reared up and threw Mr Brown to the ground. He must have banged his head because he fell asleep.

When he woke up he could not move. He was tied to the back of a horse. A dozen Sioux Indians were whooping and shouting and dancing round him. Soon he could see the camp to which he was being led.

They tied him to a carved pole in the middle of their village. Six young braves lined up facing him. The nearest one took an arrow from his quiver. He fixed it to his bow. He took careful aim at his target — **TWANG!** He let the arrow go.

It was just at that moment that Mrs Brown
came to say that the coffee was ready. Seeing
Mr Brown fast asleep, she tapped him lightly on
the shoulder.

Mr Brown awoke with a start. He clutched his
arm. He thought it was the arrow that had
hit him.

"What a nightmare!" he exclaimed.

"You will have to stop eating such an
enormous Sunday lunch, dear," said
Mrs Brown.

The Great Jumping Contest

A flea and a grasshopper met one day.

The flea was very proud of his jumping. "I can jump higher than you," he said.

"Let me see you jump," said the grasshopper.

The flea gave a mighty jump.

"Beat that," he said.

The grasshopper said, "Easy!" He leapt high into the air.

"See, that jump was higher than yours."

"No, it wasn't," said the flea.

"Yes, it was," said the grasshopper.

"Mine was higher," said the flea.

"Yours was lower," said the grasshopper.

"Everybody knows that I can jump higher than any other animal," boasted the flea.

"Rubbish!" shouted the grasshopper.

They went on quarrelling until late in the
night. They made so much noise that the other
animals could not get to sleep.

It was the owl who got them to be quiet in the
end. "Wait till tomorrow," he said. "I will ask
our king to decide who is the better jumper."

The two animals agreed to this. They went to
sleep at last, and so did all the others.

The next day King Lion was told all about the
quarrel. "Bring the two boasters to me
immediately," he said.

The flea and the grasshopper were brought
before him.

"Your quarrel has given me a good idea," the
king said. "You two are not the only ones who
can jump. I will hold a great jumping contest.
Then I will find out who can jump the highest
in my kingdom."

News of the contest spread. The flea and the grasshopper were joined by a kangaroo and a frog.

They all went into training, except for the frog. He preferred to sit on a water lily and sleep most of the time.

The flea got a great pile of bricks. He started with five bricks, one on top of the other. He jumped these, and then got his friends to put on another one. He kept practising until he could jump over a hundred bricks. Soon he ran out of bricks. He was jumping so high you couldn't see him without a telescope.

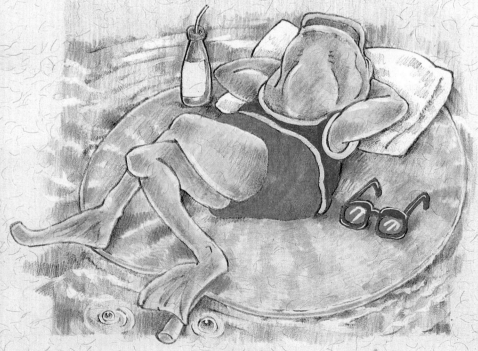

The grasshopper practised jumping and singing. He wanted to be good at both. He was not jumping half as high as the flea.

The kangaroo practised too hard. He made so many big jumps that he forgot how to do little ones. He tried to jump through the door of his house. He jumped too hard and crashed through the roof. That was the end of him.

On the morning of the contest, most animals expected the flea to win.

The king declared the contest open.

The flea was the first to jump. He jumped so high that he vanished out of sight. He never came down again.

The grasshopper jumped very high. He sang a song all the way up. He sang another song on the way down. He landed very lightly and gave a bow. All the animals cheered like mad.

They had to wake up the frog when his turn came. Yawning sleepily he made his jump. He hardly left the ground. He just went high enough to land on the king's paw.

Then the king spoke up.

"The flea has not made a jump at all," he said. "When you jump, you should come down again. The flea did not come down. He went flying instead. This is not a flying contest."

The grasshopper looked pleased. He was sure he was going to win now.

The king went on. "The grasshopper jumped very well. He sang sweetly too. He might have jumped higher but for his singing. That stopped him from thinking how to jump the highest. No, the one who jumped highest of all was the frog. I declare him the winner."

The grasshopper was angry. "I jumped much higher than the frog," he complained. "I should be the winner."

All the other animals agreed. (Except for the frog. He was fast asleep on the king's paw.)

"The frog hardly jumped at all. The grasshopper should be the winner," they said.

The king raised a paw. "Silence!" he said. "The frog was the only one to *think* about the contest. Don't forget, we are trying to find who jumped the highest."

The animals still looked puzzled. (All except the frog. He was snoring peacefully on the king's paw.)

"Tell me this," said the king. "Who is the highest person in the land?"

"Why, you are, your majesty. Nobody can be higher than the king," they told him.

"Exactly," said the king. "That is why the frog has won. He jumped as high as me. So he, too, must be the highest in the land. Now let us give three cheers for the winner."

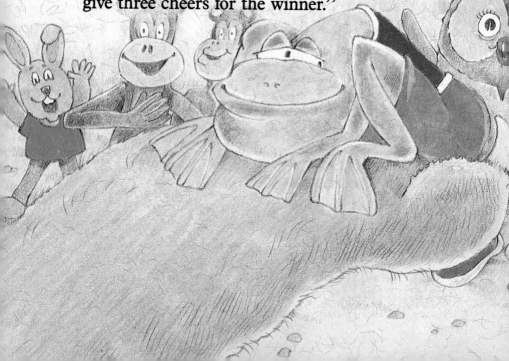

They gave three cheers. They sang 'For he's a jolly good fellow'. They sang so loudly that they even woke up the frog. All, that is, except for the grasshopper.

For once, he had nothing to sing about.

The Filthy Stranger

Once a stranger came to an inn. No one had
ever seen a man so filthy. His shoes were
covered with mud. They looked as if they had
not been cleaned for years. His clothes were
dirty and full of grease and stains. His hair was
tangled and matted. It had not seen a comb for
many months.

The stranger came up
to the innkeeper.

"I want a room,"
he said.

The innkeeper did not
want such a filthy man
in his inn. It might
upset his other guests.
So he said to the
stranger, "It's more than
a room you want. You
could do with a
good bath."

"You do know what a bath is?" asked the innkeeper.

"Of course I know what a bath is," replied the stranger. "I've eaten dozens of them in my time."

It was the innkeeper's turn to look puzzled. "You say you've eaten dozens of baths in your time," he said. "What do they look like then?"

"I'll tell you," answered the stranger. "They have wings."

"Wings?" said the innkeeper. He could hardly believe his ears.

"Yes, wings," said the stranger. "They have the same kind of wings as donkeys."

The innkeeper said, "Now I *know* that you have never seen a bath." Then he added, "And you haven't seen a donkey either!"

33

One Good Turn Deserves Another

Far, far from any town, a tribe of rabbits once lived happily.

It was a lonely place. No one ever came that way to disturb them. On fine days, they would play in the sun at peace. On dull days they slept, safe and snug in their burrows.

Then, one day a terrible thing happened. A wild horse came galloping by. No horse had ever been that way before. The rabbits did not expect such a thing. They had no time to get out of the way. So many of them were trampled by the heavy hooves.

When the horse had gone, the rabbits were shocked at the number of the dead. For hours they wept in sorrow.

One rabbit then said, "We must stop this weeping. It will not bring back our loved ones. It was an awful thing to happen. We must make sure that it does not happen again."

"What can we do?" asked the other rabbits.

Their leader spoke up. "If the horse gallops this way again, it will be the end of us all. There are two things we can do. We can move to another place. Or, we can ask the horse to keep away from here."

One rabbit said, "We have been happy here. It has been a good place to make our burrows."

The others agreed.

The leader said, "Then we must ask the horse to keep away."

"He might not like that," said one old rabbit. "He might be angry and decide to trample us all to death."

"We have not much choice," said the leader. "I myself will go to the horse. If I do not come back, you will know I have been crushed by his hooves. You will then have to move and find a new home."

The brave leader set off.

He followed the scent of the horse and found him drinking at the river.

The rabbit bowed low. "Good horse, may I speak with you?" he said.

The horse stopped drinking. "What do you want?" he asked.

The rabbit told him what had happened. "Hundreds of rabbits have died today," he said.

"For that I am sorry," said the horse. "I did not know there were rabbits there."

"No. You would not see them. Most of them would be sleeping in their burrows. They would be just below the ground," said the rabbit.

"What a shame!" said the horse. "I was only going to the river to drink."

"Do you think you could go to the river by another way?" asked the rabbit. He then told the horse exactly where the rabbits had their homes. They were some distance from the river so that they would be safe from floods.

"So, if I keep close to the river I will not disturb you," said the horse.

"If you could do that, we would be most grateful," the rabbit replied.

"In future, that is what I shall do." said the horse. "Please tell your friends how sorry I am for what has happened. From now on they will be in no danger from me."

"You are most kind," said the rabbit. "In return, I promise you this. If you are ever in trouble, we rabbits will come to help you."

"I can't think how such timid rabbits could ever help me," said the horse. "But thank you all the same."

"You never know," the rabbit said. "You can't have too many friends."

The rabbit came back and told his tribe the good news. They were delighted. Soon they were playing in the sun or sleeping in their burrows without fear.

Unknown to the horse, some men had been
following him for days. He was a fine horse and
would bring a good price at market. But first
they would have to catch him and tame him. To
catch him would not be easy. They could not
shoot him or hurt him. No one would buy a
damaged horse. They would have to catch him
in a trap, alive and well.

The men kept watch on the horse. They saw
that he went to drink in the river every evening.
He went at the same time and drank at the same
spot. He always went by the same route.

One day the men dug a deep pit. They covered it with branches and put fresh grass on top. Then they hid nearby.

Soon the horse came by. He saw the fresh grass and went to eat it. The ground gave way under his feet.

He was trapped.

The men came out from hiding. They were pleased to catch such a fine horse. They looked him over. He was frightened, but unharmed.

It was getting late, so the men left the horse in the pit for the night. They would come next day with spades and ropes to take him away.

When the men had gone, the horse looked at his prison. He kicked at the steep walls in fury. His fury soon gave way to fear. As dusk came, he began to neigh piteously. Loud and long his moans travelled into the night.

Far away, the rabbits heard the strange sounds.

"What noise is that?" they asked a passing bird who was late getting home to his nest.

"Don't you rabbits know anything?" asked the bird. "That is the sound of a horse, and he is in trouble. I have just flown over there. He is caught in a deep pit. There was nothing I could do to help him."

The leader called the rabbits together. "This could be our friend," he said. "I promised we would help him if ever we could. Now seems to be the time."

He sent for help to other tribes of rabbits. Soon thousands of rabbits were on the march. They followed the moans of the horse and came to the pit.

The rabbits' leader spoke up. "We have come to rescue you," he said.

"Rabbits?" the horse gasped. All he could see were thousands of rabbits on every side. "It would take an elephant to lift me out of here. What good can rabbits do?"

"Wait and see," said the chief rabbit. "We may not be good at lifting, but we can burrow."

And burrow they did. Thousands of them. They moved ton after ton of earth. As one rabbit tired, another took his place. A huge tunnel was dug from the pit. All night long the work went on.

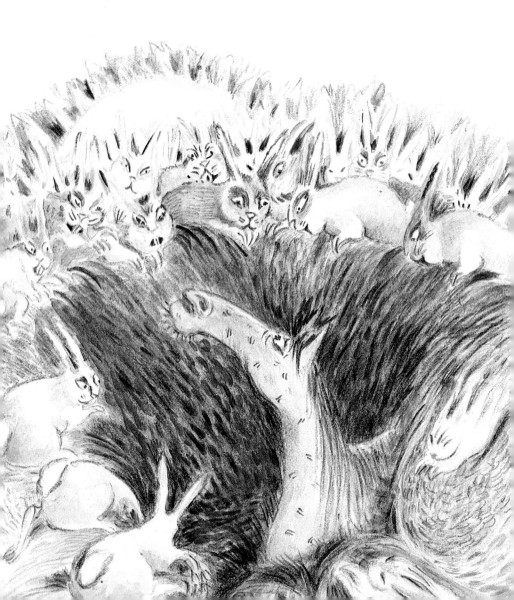

Dawn was almost breaking as the last of the
earth was moved. The horse walked safely to
the surface as thousands of rabbits cheered
like mad.

"Thank you, my friend," said the horse
before he galloped away. "How right you were,
rabbit. You can't have too many friends."

The Giant in the Bottle

Once, long ago, a soldier was making his way
home from the wars.

To get to his home, he had to cross a thick
forest. He had been walking for many days, and
he was very tired.

When night came, he was still only half way
through the trees. There was no moon and no
light from the stars. A thick fog came down.
Soon the soldier was hopelessly lost. He wrapped
his cloak round him and slept at the foot of
a tree.

When morning came, he found himself in a part of the forest where he had never been before. Patches of fog still hung over the ground. There was no sound, not even the song of a bird.

Suddenly he heard a voice calling faintly, "Let me out. Let me out."

As he walked on the voice grew louder. Then the fog cleared and he found himself at the mouth of a cave. He looked all around, but there was nobody there. Still the voice went on shouting, "Let me out. Let me out."

The soldier was puzzled. He was just about to leave when he saw a glint of something bright at the back of the cave. It was a bottle. The soldier picked it up and took it outside. Then, very loudly indeed, the voice shouted, "Let me out. Let me out." The soldier nearly dropped the bottle in surprise. And no wonder!

The voice was coming from inside the bottle.

The soldier held the bottle up to the light. Black smoke billowed and swirled inside the bottle. Yet there was no fire. The cork was quite tight in the neck of the bottle. The smoke could not get out, but the sound of the voice did. By now it was extremely loud. "Let me out. Let me out," it bellowed.

The soldier pulled the cork out of the bottle.
The thick black smoke poured out. Up and up it
climbed. Round and round it swirled. When it
had made a cloud as big as a tree, it stopped
growing. Then the smoke slowly turned into the
shape of a man. First appeared the head. Then
the body. Lastly the arms and legs. But it was no
ordinary man. It was a giant, bigger than the
tallest tree in the forest.

"Who are you?" asked the soldier.

"I am the spirit of the forest," boomed the giant in a voice like thunder.

"How did you come to be in that bottle?" asked the soldier. Though he was afraid, he was curious too.

"Many years ago," said the giant, "I had an enemy. He was a great magician. He cast a spell on me which made me as small as an ant. Small as I was, he dropped me into a bottle. He changed me into a cloud of smoke. Then he corked the bottle and hid it in a cave. I have been there until you set me free."

"I am glad to have helped you," said
the soldier.

"You should be sorry," said the giant. "I was
cursed to stay in the bottle for ever or to kill the
one who sets me free."

The giant then picked up the soldier and held
him high above the trees.

"See," he said. "I will drop you from here.
You will fall like a stone. You should be glad of
such a death. It will be quick and you will feel
no pain."

The soldier pleaded with him. "I set you free
and gave you your life back. Please spare mine."

"I cannot," said the giant. "The curse is too
strong. I must obey it."

The soldier's heart was seized with terror, yet he kept a cool head.

"This is some sort of trick," he said. "You are enormous. Nobody as big as you could fit into so small a bottle."

The giant placed the soldier back on the ground.

"Are you calling me a liar?" he roared.

"Well, it does take some believing," said the soldier.

"We spirits do not lie," thundered the giant. "Watch."

Slowly the giant turned back into a cloud of smoke. First his arms and legs disappeared. Then his body. Lastly his head. Then the cloud shrank. When it was quite small it drifted back into the bottle. When all the smoke was inside, the soldier sprang forward. In a flash he rammed the cork firmly into the bottle. He placed the bottle carefully at the back of the cave. He forgot that he had been tired. He ran and ran until he had left that place far behind.

It is not likely that you will ever find that cave. It is in a country a long way from here. But if you do, I trust that you will run as the soldier did and leave the cave, and its bottle, far, far behind.